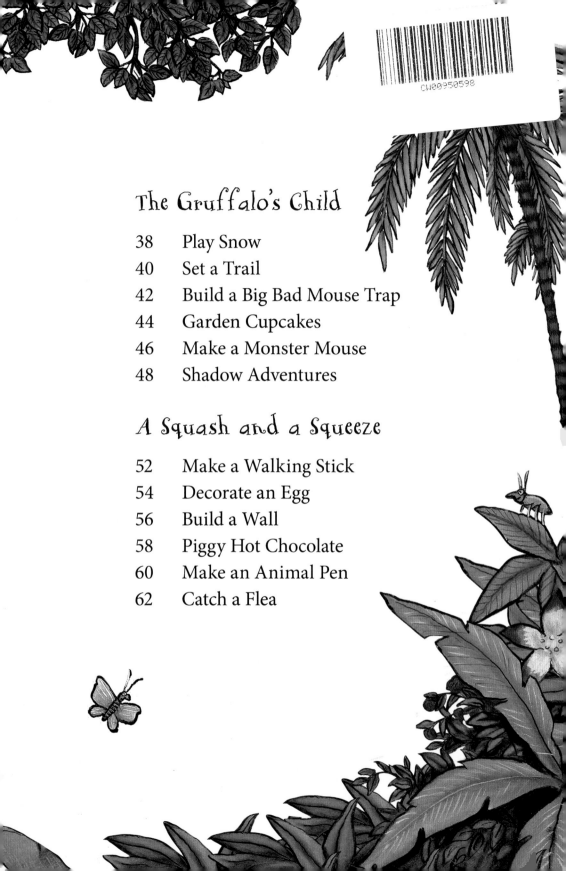

The Gruffalo's Child

38 Play Snow

40 Set a Trail

42 Build a Big Bad Mouse Trap

44 Garden Cupcakes

46 Make a Monster Mouse

48 Shadow Adventures

A Squash and a Squeeze

52 Make a Walking Stick

54 Decorate an Egg

56 Build a Wall

58 Piggy Hot Chocolate

60 Make an Animal Pen

62 Catch a Flea

A Letter from Little Wild Things

Dear adventurers,

We are Little Wild Things, a small community organisation running outdoor nature play sessions for children in a West Oxfordshire woodland. We spend our days outside with local families sploshing in mud, mixing up potions, digging for treasure and racing snails, and we really can't think of anything we enjoy more.

Children today spend less time playing outdoors than ever before, so we want to spread the word that outdoor play is fun and easy. Most of us have a bit of grass or patch of muddy ground within walking distance, and there is always something exciting going on in the natural world. Birds might be singing, leaves might be falling, or there might just be hundreds of huge puddles to jump in. Playing outside together is fun and free and is likely to lead to healthier, happier children. But the best thing? Nature is something you can never grow out of.

This book is a collection of some of our favourite outdoor adventures based on four much-loved picture books by Julia Donaldson and Axel Scheffler.

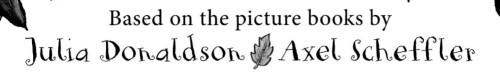

Based on the picture books by
Julia Donaldson 🍃 Axel Scheffler

The Snail
and the
Whale
and Friends
Outdoor
Activity
Book

Activities created by
Little Wild Things

MACMILLAN CHILDREN'S BOOKS

Contents

4   A Letter from Little Wild Things

6   Hints and Tips

The Snail and the Whale

10   Make an Adventure Bag

12   Snail Races

14   Make a Whale Friend

16   Snail Salad

18   Erupting Volcanoes

20   Try a Sensory Story

The Smartest Giant in Town

24   Mini Roads

26   A House for a Mouse

28   Build a Tiny Tent

30   Muddy Bog

32   Barefoot Walk

34   Be a Giant

Use them for a party, in the school holidays, on a walk, or on a rainy day. Get outside and go wild, and we hope you have as much fun with them as we do.

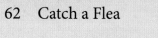

little wild things

Good for a rainy day ...

14 Make a Whale Friend
20 Try a Sensory Story
38 Play Snow
54 Decorate an Egg

Good for the garden ...

16 Snail Salad
28 Build a Tiny Tent
40 Set a Trail
42 Build a Big Bad Mouse Trap

Good for messy play ...

18 Erupting Volcanoes
30 Muddy Bog
56 Build a Wall

Good for doing on a walk ...

10 Make an Adventure Bag
26 A House for a Mouse
48 Shadow Adventures

Good for a party ...

32 Barefoot Walk
44 Garden Cupcakes
46 Make a Monster Mouse
58 Piggy Hot Chocolate

Good for keeping busy ...

12 Snail Races
24 Mini Roads
52 Make a Walking Stick
60 Make an Animal Pen

Good for letting off steam ...

34 Be a Giant
62 Catch a Flea

Hints and Tips

Are you ready to get adventuring? Here are some hints and tips to read before you start.

You'll need to ask a grown-up to help you set up and lend a hand here and there.

Before you start any activity, read through the instructions with your grown-up and gather all the things you need for your adventure kit. You'll find a list at the beginning of every activity.

Ask your grown-up to help with anything you find especially difficult. Cutting things out with scissors, folding or measuring can all be hard work. Sometimes you'll just need your grown-up to show you what to do and, with a bit of practice, you'll be doing it by yourself in no time.

Your outdoors doesn't have to be big and wild! Any garden, park or patch of outside space will do for lots of the activities in this book.

Sometimes you'll want to collect things from your garden or park or dig in a flower bed. Check with a grown-up that you are allowed to do those things before you start.

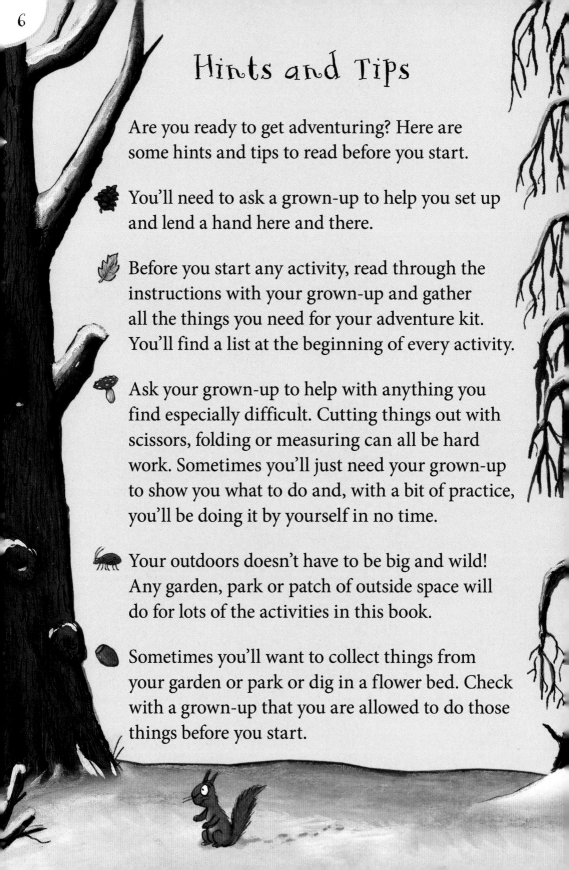

Remember it's always best to collect things that are on the ground rather than picking living flowers and plants. For example, you should always take sticks from the ground rather than pulling them off trees.

It's great to get messy, and lots of these activities involve mud, so it's best not to try them when you're wearing your smartest clothes! Also, be sure to give your hands a good wash with hot water and soap when you've finished playing.

Lots of the things you can make in this book might look delicious, but remember anything you make outdoors is not for eating.

Take care of your friends if you're running, jumping or swishing things around. Make sure you have plenty of space so you don't bang, bash or bump them by mistake.

Now you know all there is to know and you're ready to start adventuring! What will you do first?

The Snail and the Whale

"The sea is deep and the world is wide!
How I long to sail!"
Said the tiny snail.

The tiny snail longs for adventure and hitches a
lift on the tail of a great big, grey-blue humpback
whale as they head off to see the world. Together
they see towering icebergs, golden beaches and fiery
mountains, but when the tide goes out and the whale
is beached in a bay, it's up to the tiny snail to come up
with a plan big enough to save him.

Turn the page to start your very own adventure!
Race a snail, create a sock whale friend and explore
your senses with a very special version of the story.

Make an Adventure Bag

The world is wide and there's lots to explore. Where will you go today?
Make this brilliant adventure bag to take with you.

Adventure kit:

- A 30cm by 30cm square of pale material
- Felt tip pens
- An elastic band
- Some special things to take on your adventure

What to do:

1. First find a stick long enough that if you hold one end in your hand and put it over your shoulder, the other end will reach to just above your head. Try a few sticks out until you find one that's just the right length and weight.

2. Next lay out your square of material and use your pens to decorate it. Will you have stars and squiggles or stripes and spots?

3. Now decide what essential things you will need to take on your adventure. How about a notebook, your favourite toy or a pile of conkers?

4. Lay your material on the ground, colourful side down. Place your special items into the centre of the material.

5. Bring the four corners of the material into the middle and wrap the elastic band around them to hold them together (you might need a grown-up to help you).

6. You are now ready to insert your stick. There should be four holes in the top part of your material, under the elastic band. Push your stick into one hole and out of the hole diagonally opposite.

7. Hoist the bag onto your shoulder and give it a little wiggle until it sits comfortably. Now test your bag to make sure it is secure – try a small leap, march up and down and turn round and round on the spot. If the bag slips you can make it fit more tightly by pulling the four corners of the material outwards so the elastic band rolls down towards the stick.

8. You are now all set for your adventure – where will you go first?

Hints and tips:

🌸 If you don't have an elastic band, a hair tie or a piece of string will work just as well, or you can always tie the two sets of diagonal corners together to secure your bag.

🌸 Remember to leave a bit of space in your bag so that you can add in any treasures you find while on your adventure.

Keep adventuring:

Could you make your teddy their own adventure bag? Follow the instructions in just the same way but make everything a bit smaller!

Snail Races

The tiny snail saves the day by racing for help.
Hold your own snail race to find the fastest snail of all!

Adventure kit:

- A bucket or pot
- A piece of chalk
- A bowl of water
- A smooth surface for your racetrack like a paving slab

What to do:

1. First find some snails. Snails like damp, dark places and can often be found under stones, logs or flowerpots. Once you've found one, lift it carefully from its place by holding its shell and pop it in your bucket or pot. You'll need at least one snail for each person playing.

2. Now prepare your racetrack. Draw a circle in the centre of your paving slab to be the starting ring.

3. Place all the snails inside the starting ring and decide which one you will be cheering for.

4. Give your snails plenty of time to come out of their shells and look around. You can think of some names for the racers while you're waiting.

5. Snails find it much easier to move on damp surfaces and so usually race better if the track is a little bit wet. Dip your fingers in the bowl of water and drip water over the track to help them go faster.

6. Once the snails start crawling, give them lots of encouragement – everyone loves being cheered for after all. The first snail to make it to the edge of the paving slab is the winner!

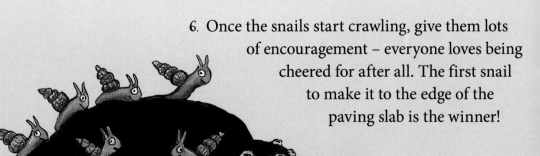

7. Now they have the hang of it, pop your snails back in the starting circle and race them again to see who is the champion crawler.

8. Put your snails back where you found them once you have finished racing.

Hints and tips:

❋ It's usually easier to find snails in the early morning when it's cooler and damper.

❋ Remember that snails are living creatures so be very gentle with them, and only ever pick them up by their shells.

❋ Snails are herbivores and love eating green leaves. Try putting a leaf at the end of the racetrack to see if it will make your champions even faster!

Keep adventuring:

Try putting some obstacles in the path of any super speedy snails. Can they climb over a stick or will they go around it? Watch the snails closely to see how they come out of their shells and how they travel along. The bottom of a snail is called its 'foot' and it is very strong and full of muscle. Using this foot, snails can crawl up and down and even upside down! Slugs also make good racers so why not have a whole slimy sports day?

Make a Whale Friend

This is the whale who came one night
When the tide was high and the stars were bright.
Learn how to make your very own humpback whale out of an old sock.

Adventure Kit:

- A grown-up's old sock
- Safety scissors
- Some soil
- A spoon
- An elastic band
- Double-sided tape
- Two buttons
- Cress seeds
- Some water

What to do:

1. Lay your sock out flat and carefully cut off the top third. Put the cut-off piece to one side for later.

2. Now use your spoon to fill the sock three quarters full with soil. Ask a grown-up to hold the sock open to help you get the soil right to the bottom.

3. Wrap an elastic band around the open end of the sock so that the soil is held inside. Your sock whale should now look a bit like a tadpole, with a big fat body and a flappy tail.

4. Cut out a wide triangle from the middle of the tail section so that it is the same shape as a whale's tail.

5. Take the spare piece of sock from step 1 and cut out two fin shapes.

6. Stick these fins onto your whale's body and the button eyes onto its head using some small squares of double-sided tape.

7. Push the soil around inside your whale until it is the shape you want it to be.

8. On your whale's back, pinch a small bit of sock between your thumb and finger. Pull this up and cut off the pinched bit to make a hole around 1cm across. This is your whale's blowhole.

9. Sprinkle some cress seeds into the blowhole, then pop your whale onto a sunny windowsill. Pour a little water into its blowhole each day and soon your cress will start growing. The cress will make it look like your whale is spouting water!

Hints and tips:

🌸 The whale in the story is a humpback whale. These whales have eyes and fins on the sides of their body. Look at the pictures in your storybook to check where to place yours.

🌸 If you don't have any buttons, use little circles of card or some small stones for your whale's eyes instead.

Keep adventuring:

Once your cress has grown big and tall, snip it off and use it to sprinkle over a salad or add it to a sandwich. Then sow some more cress seeds to start the growing all over again. How many different sized socks can you find to make whales with? Perhaps you could make a whole family! Why not try finding an empty snail shell to pop on your whale's tail too?

Snail Salad

Even the most adventurous of snails will need to stop for a snack sooner or later. Help your slimy friends to dine out in style!

Adventure kit: Somewhere with lots of greenery, safety scissors and some plastic plates or flat stones.

What to do:

1. Start by gathering the ingredients for your salad. You will need a selection of grasses, leaves, petals and even some herbs if you have them. Try and collect a variety of colours and textures so that your salad looks really exciting!

2. Using your scissors, take a piece of grass or a leaf and snip it in half. Then keep snipping each piece in half until you have a pile of snail bite-sized pieces.

3. Repeat step 2 with the rest of your leaves and petals until you have four or five piles of different ingredients.

4. You are now ready to create your salad! First decide which ingredients you will include on each plate, then think about how you will present it. Will you sprinkle the ingredients all over the plate, or make lots of little piles? Why not try making a pattern or even a smiley face?

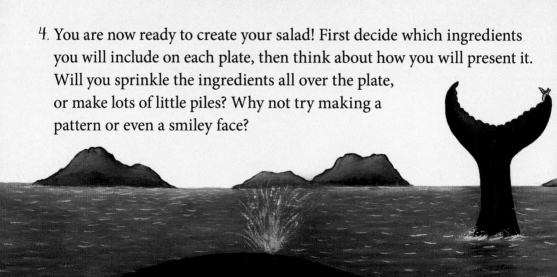

5. Once your salad plates are ready, find a place to display them. How many different types of salad can you come up with? Can you create a truly mouth-watering menu for your garden guests?

Hints and tips:

🌸 Make sure to check with a grown-up before you pick or cut anything.

🌸 Your salads would look wonderful displayed on a colourful tablecloth, so why not colour in some paper or use an old bit of material under your plates?

🌸 Remember that these salads are just for snails and not for you to chew on!

Keep adventuring:

Could you make a special salad dressing by whisking up some soil and water to finish your plates to perfection? Try leaving your salad plates out overnight, then checking them in the morning to see if any new friends have had a nibble.

Erupting Volcanoes

The snail sees all sorts of exciting things on her adventure, even mountains blowing out fire! Can you make a mini fiery mountain?

Adventure kit:

- Soil, sand or rocks to build your volcano
- Leaves, sticks and stones
- A small bottle with a long neck, like a food colouring bottle
- Water
- Red food colouring
- Vinegar
- Bicarbonate of soda
- Three cups or bowls
- A lolly stick
- A pipette or a plastic syringe

What to do:

1. Find a good spot to build your volcano, somewhere you can make messy!

2. Take the soil, sand or rocks and start by building a mound like a mole hill. Then make a hole in the top and push the bottle in, leaving about 1cm sticking out.

3. Add some geological features to the sides of the mound. Leaves or sticks can be mini-trees and piles of pebbles can become boulders. This is your volcano.

4. Take the three cups or bowls and fill one halfway with vinegar, one halfway with bicarbonate of soda, and one halfway with water. Add a few drops of red food colouring to the water to make the lava flow red. Now you are ready for an eruption!

5. Using the pipette or plastic syringe add the coloured water to your bottle until it reaches the bottom of the neck.

6. Next take the lolly stick and add five big heaps of bicarbonate of soda to the bottle.

7. Now fill your pipette with vinegar, then push it to the very bottom of the bottle and squeeze all the vinegar in nice and quickly.

8. Sit back and watch your volcano erupt and red lava flow down the sides! Are any of your trees knocked over by the flowing lava? How far does it travel?

9. Keep adding vinegar to your volcano until it stops erupting. Once it has finished, give the bottle a rinse with some water and follow the steps once more to make your volcano erupt again.

Hints and tips:

🌸 If you don't have a lolly stick, the handle of a teaspoon works just as well.

🌸 If you don't have a pipette or a syringe just pour the vinegar in using a teaspoon or a small jug.

Keep adventuring:

Can you make volcanoes of different shapes and sizes? Try placing some small plastic toys around your volcano. Will they be able to escape before the lava gets to them?

Try a Sensory Story

Can you hear, feel, smell and taste the story?

Adventure kit: *The Snail and the Whale* story book, some sensory props like those suggested below, a tray or table to put your props on, a scarf or a strip of material to be a blindfold and someone to read the story.

What to do:

We all love the story of *The Snail and the Whale*, but have you ever tried reading it without looking at the pictures? In this activity, you will be using your other senses to experience the story by using a variety of props. There might be something to touch, something to listen to and occasionally even something to smell or taste! Try not to look at the props before you start so you'll be surprised by all the different sensations . . . Ready for the challenge? Then read on!

First ask a grown-up to collect all the props you'll need and lay them out on a tray or table. Then put on your blindfold and make sure there are no holes for you to peep through!

Ask your grown-up to read the story aloud, and every time a certain thing is mentioned, give you something to feel, hear, smell or taste. For example, when the snail's trail is mentioned, they can run a wet paintbrush over the back of your hand to feel like the slimy trail. Instead of using your eyes to look at the pictures, you'll be using your other senses so the story really comes to life in your imagination!

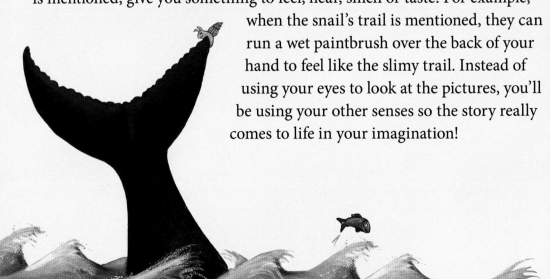

Sensory prop suggestions:

Use half
a grape to feel
like the slimy
snail

Use a grain
of salt to taste
like the sea

Use a
banana to feel
like the tail of
the whale

Use an ice
cube to feel like
an iceberg

Flick droplets
of water to feel like
the spray keeping the
whale cool

Bang a
metal pan with a
spoon to sound like
the school bell

Pour water
between two
containers to sound
like crashing
waves

Use a bottle
of suncream to
smell like
summer

Hints and tips:

✿ We use our eyes all the time. By covering them up we give our other senses a chance to really shine, so try hard not to peep!

✿ Once you get the hang of it, see what other props you can use to make the story even more exciting!

Keep adventuring:

Once your grown-up has read the story to you, why not get them to put the blindfold on so you can do a sensory story for them? You can try this idea with any of your favourite picture books or use your super senses to hear, smell and touch the world around you when you're next out on a walk.

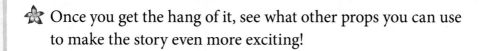

The Smartest GIANT in Town

"Look me up and down –
I'm the smartest giant in town!"

George the giant is fed up with his scruffy old gown and
sandals, so he decides to buy some smart new clothes.
But when he meets some animals who need his help, he
ends up giving them all away until . . . oh no! Now he's
the coldest giant in town! Luckily his dear old gown and
sandals are waiting for him back at the shop, along with
all his new friends who have a special surprise for George.

Read on to find out how to build your own tiny tent,
tickle your toes with a barefoot walk and even become
a giant yourself!

Mini Roads

George is a giant, so the town must seem tiny to him! Try building yourself a mini road to play with and you can feel like a giant too!

Adventure Kit:
Lots and lots of sticks, some toy cars, trucks and tractors and a flat outdoor space to build your mini road.

What to do:

1. Take a stick and lay it on the ground.

2. Lay a second stick parallel to the first stick, leaving enough space between them for your cars to drive. The sticks will mark the edges of your road.

3. Take another stick and lay it end to end with the first stick. Then lay another stick end to end with the second stick. Keep adding sticks in this way to build up your road.

4. Once you have a short section of road, test your cars in it to make sure they have plenty of room to race along. Decide whether you want to leave enough space for two cars to go past each other or whether there will only be single-file traffic.

5. Now add to your road by continuing to build up the two lines of sticks. Will your road be long and straight, go around corners or perhaps even in a big circle?

6. When your road is as long as you want it to be, get your cars and trucks out and start driving.

7. Once you've had a good drive around on your road, see how inventive you can be with it. Can you create a carpark or build a tunnel for your cars to zoom through? Perhaps there are piles of sand and stones that need to be moved from one place to another – can your trucks and tractors do the job?

8. Now you've built your mini road, pretend to be a giant like George to see how it feels to be the biggest thing in town. Can you cross your road in one single step? Will your giant foot stop the traffic?

Hints and tips:

🌸 Try clearing the ground of sticks, stones and leaves before you start, so the passengers in your cars won't have too much of a bumpy ride!

🌸 If the ground isn't very flat, toy cars and trucks with bigger wheels might be easier to push along.

Keep adventuring:

Imagine where your road could lead. Will it take your drivers to a tiny town, a dark cave or a picnic spot?

A House for a Mouse

The mice in the story are all sad and squeaking because their house has burnt down. Can you design a new place for them to live?

Adventure kit: An outdoor space with some interesting natural bits and pieces.

What to do:

1. First find some building materials – shells, conkers, leaves, sticks, bits of bark, little logs, pebbles, flowers and feathers are all great.

2. Next, find a fabulous place to create your house. Will it be under a tree, inside a log, in a patch of long grass or beside a stone?

3. Clear the ground before you start building by brushing away loose sticks and leaves.

4. Start by building the roof of your house. You can use a bit of bark propped up with a stick or leaning against a tree, tie together the tops of some long growing grass or push leaves onto sticks stuck in the ground.

5. Fill in any gaps around the outside with sticks, moss or leaves so your mouse family can stay nice and snuggly – just don't forget to leave a door!

6. Now think about what your mice will need inside their house. How about a log kitchen table and some pebble chairs, or some feather beds with leaf blankets? What can you find for the mouse children to play with and can you fill the larder with tasty nuts for all the family?

7. As well as a house, any mouse family would love a garden to play in. Could you make a stick seesaw, a moss trampoline or a leaf slide? Don't forget to build a fence around the garden to keep the children safe.

8. Once you're happy that your mouse house is everything you want it to be, give your grown-up a tour!

Hints and tips:

🌸 Be as creative as you can be. If you're stuck for ideas, think about what things you have in your house, or wish you did!

Keep adventuring:

On your way home, keep your eyes open for signs that there are mice about – tiny paths, small holes in the ground or nibbled nuts and berries. Perhaps they'll come on holiday to your mouse mansion!

Build a Tiny Tent

The fox uses George's sock as a cosy sleeping bag, but he might need a tent if it rains! Try building one for him and any other animals who might fancy a spot of camping.

Adventure kit:

- A selection of sticks
- Two short bits of string
- A piece of material
- Safety scissors
- Your teddies

What to do:

1. First prepare your materials. You will need five long sticks about as long as your grown-up's arm, four medium sticks as long as your own arm, and four short fat sticks to be tent pegs. Your piece of material should be one grown-up arm wide and two grown-up arms long.

2. Next, find a flat place and make a square on the ground using the four medium sticks.

3. Take four of the long sticks and push them into the ground – one at each corner of the square.

4. Now make the front of your tent frame. Take the top of two of the long sticks and pull them towards each other so they just cross over to make a triangle. If they feel wobbly just wiggle the sticks back into the earth to secure them. Now make the back of your tent frame in the same way with the other two sticks.

5. Take the last long stick and lay it across the top of your two triangles. This will make the tent roof. Next wrap string around the tops of each triangle

where all three sticks meet and tie it tight. You have a tent frame!

6. Now take your piece of material and lay it over the frame. Your material should completely cover the frame with a little bit touching the ground on all four sides.

7. Use your scissors to cut a small hole in the material at the base of each stick. Then pull the material tight over the frame and push a short fat stick into each hole to peg the tent to the ground.

8. Cut a straight line up the middle of the material at the front of your tent to make two flaps to be the doors.

9. Now grab your teddies and fill your tent with some lovely soft things for them to sleep on. Moss, grass, feathers or leaves – what will you find?

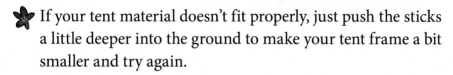

Hints and tips:

🌸 If your tent material doesn't fit properly, just push the sticks a little deeper into the ground to make your tent frame a bit smaller and try again.

🌸 If the ground is really hard and dry, ask a grown-up to help you push in the sticks.

Keep adventuring:

Why not use an old sock to make a sleeping bag for your teddy? Will your teddies need a little pretend fire outside to toast marshmallows on? You could even try putting up lots of tents to make a whole teddy campsite!

Muddy Bog

George gives his belt to a dog to make a safe dry path across the bog.
Can you create a bog and then build a path across it?

Adventure kit:

- A large tray or tin
- A spoon
- Some soil
- A jug of water
- Moss, grass and sticks
- Stones, sticks, leaves or shells to create a safe dry path
- Some small toys or teddies

What to do:

1. First you need to build your bog! Spoon lots of soil into your tray and pour in water a little at a time, then mix it all up to make a lovely, muddy bog.

2. See if you can make your bog look super realistic with little tufts of grass or patches of moss. You could even push some sticks into it to look like mini trees.

3. Once you're happy with your bog, it's time to build a safe dry path. You can do this any way you like, using stones, sticks, leaves, shells or a mixture of all four! Carefully build your path all the way from one side of

the bog to the other. Will it be long and wiggly or short and straight? Will it have to go round any pools of water or patches of moss?

4. Now grab your toys and test your path! Can they cross the bog safely without getting mucky or do they sink into the mud and get stuck? Will they run across the path, jump from stone to stone or tiptoe carefully?

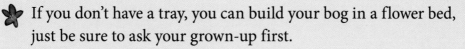

Hints and tips:

🌸 If you don't have a tray, you can build your bog in a flower bed, just be sure to ask your grown-up first.

🌸 Plastic toys work best for this game as they might need to take a little bath once you've finished to wash off all the mud!

Keep adventuring:

If your bog path is a success, why not try adding a bridge to your path to help your toys get over the muddiest bits? If you have some sand, see if you can make an area of sinking sand by mixing it with lots of water. Then your toys really will have to cross carefully!

Barefoot Walk

George is so busy giving away his clothes to animals in need that he ends up with a bare foot and needs to hop home! Do you dare to bare your feet?

Adventure Kit: Some buckets and trays, an old towel, and anything you can find to walk on – soil, leaves, water, sawdust, sticks, stones, grass etc.

What to do:

1. First find a nice flat place to set up your barefoot walk.

2. Now lay out the things you're going to walk on. Put materials out in small sections, one after the other, making each section long enough so that you can take a few steps in each different thing. For example, you might start with a bucket of water, followed by a patch of grass cuttings, then a line of sticks, a section of damp soil and a tray of stones. You can put your sections in a straight line, or go round in a circle, whichever you like best.

3. Once your sections are all laid out and ready, it's time to test your walk and let your feet do some feeling! Take off your shoes and socks and get ready.

4. Decide where you'll start, then walk slowly through each section, giving your toes plenty of time to wiggle about in each material. Which feels the nicest and which is yucky or makes you shiver? Can you think of words to describe what your toes are feeling?

5. Once you've enjoyed your walk, and your feet are delightfully dirty, use the old towel to clean and dry your toes.

Hints and tips:

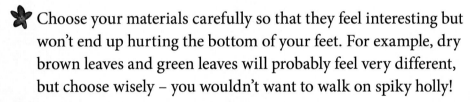 Choose your materials carefully so that they feel interesting but won't end up hurting the bottom of your feet. For example, dry brown leaves and green leaves will probably feel very different, but choose wisely – you wouldn't want to walk on spiky holly!

Make sure you walk slowly so that you don't catch your feet on any unexpected lumps and bumps.

Keep adventuring:

Try experimenting with your barefoot walk to see how many different ways there are to do it. Why not do the walk blindfolded to see if you can guess what your toes are wiggling in? Perhaps try feeling all the trays of things with your hands instead of your feet, or use your sense of smell to identify them. You could even set up an indoor barefoot walk using cushions, toys and building blocks!

Be a Giant

You may not feel all that big, but to some animals you are enormous!

Adventure Kit: Your giant self.

What to do:

George is a giant and he uses his size, and his giant clothes, to help all the animals he meets. See what you can do to help animals in your park or garden and become the kindest giant in town!

First get into your giant character . . .

- Can you stretch up to the sky and make yourself super tall?
- Can you jump up and down to make the ground shake?
- Can you jump over a puddle in a single leap?
- Can you test your strength by asking your grown-up to hold a long bit of grass or a dry twig between their hands while you try to karate chop it in half?

Now start striding about to see who might need your help!

TO GEORGE

Can you use your strong arms to break sticks and make a safe warm home for bugs?

Can you help a snail to safely cross the path?

Can you check puddles for worms that can't swim and need a helping hand?

Can you use your giant strength to move a stone from the path of an ant?

Can you collect up lots of yummy pinecones for a busy mouse family?

Can you bring water from a puddle to give a drink to a baby tree?

Can you walk carefully so you don't squash plants and animals with your giant feet?

Keep adventuring:

How many animals have you helped today? There will be animals needing help wherever you go, so keep your eyes open and your giant helping hands ready. If you feel you've done a great job, you could even make yourself a crown to wear – just like George's!

THE GRUFFALO'S CHILD

The Gruffalo said that no gruffalo should
Ever set foot in the deep dark wood.

But one wild and windy night, the Gruffalo's Child
ignores her father's warning and tiptoes out
into the snow in search of the Big Bad Mouse.
After meeting a snake, an owl and a fox, the
Gruffalo's Child starts to think the Big Bad
Mouse doesn't exist after all . . . or does he?

Read on to find out how to make your
own snow to play in, have fun with
shadows and build a Big Bad Mouse trap.

Play Snow

The snow fell fast and the wind blew wild.
Into the wood went the Gruffalo's Child.
Make some play snow for your animals to go exploring in!

Adventure Kit:

- Bicarbonate of soda (at least 300g)
- White hair conditioner
- A cup
- A big bowl
- A mixing spoon
- Sticks, stones and natural items
- Some plastic animal toys
- A tray to play in

What to do:

1. Put 3 cups of bicarbonate of soda into the big bowl.

2. Add in ½ cup of conditioner and give it a stir with the spoon.

3. Look at the amount of mixture you have. If you think you'll need more snow to play in, add another 3 cups of bicarbonate of soda and another ½ cup of conditioner.

4. Keep stirring until your mixture is crumbly but holds together when you squeeze it. Add more bicarbonate of soda if your mixture is too wet or more conditioner if your mixture doesn't hold together. This is your snow!

5. Pile your snow into the tray with the spoon or your hands. You might want to pat it all flat, make a big hill or create lots of little mounds.

6. Use sticks and natural items to make a winter scene. Could a stick be a frozen tree? Or perhaps a pile of stones could be a snow-topped mountain!

7. Add your animal toys to the snow scene to see what they make of it! Will they bury each other, roll around in it or build a snowman?

8. See what other lovely things you can do with your snow. Can you make a pile of tiny snowballs, use your toys to make footprints or make a snow slope for your animals to slide down?

Hints and tips:

● Did you notice that your play snow actually feels cold? This is because the bicarbonate of soda and conditioner react together to make the mixture you're playing with. This reaction needs heat and both materials draw in heat from around them making the mixture feel cold.

● Your snow will keep in a sealed container for a few months, so when you've had enough snow fun just pack it away for another day.

Keep adventuring:

What happens if you add vinegar to your snow? Can you build a snowman and then melt him? Your snow will need to go in the bin after this game so perhaps save it until the end!

Set a Trail

Aha! Oho! A trail in the snow!
Whose is this trail and where does it go?
The Gruffalo's Child is good at following tracks and trails.
Can you make a trail for someone to follow too?

Adventure Kit:
A collection of lots and lots of something for the trail and a prize to leave at the end.

What to do:

1. Decide what collection you will use to make your trail: pinecones, grass cuttings, leaves, conkers, stones, sticks or teddies all work well. Take your collection and put it into some kind of container that you can easily carry and move about.

2. Find a place to make your trail. How about a big bit of grass, a patio or an area of trees?

3. Think about how much space you'll have between the things in your trail. Will they be placed right next to each other or spaced far apart for your trail follower to find?

4. Lay out your trail. How long can you make it? It may have lots of twists, turns and squiggles, and it might even go back on itself! It could go up hills, round trees and down holes . . . where will it end?

5. Decide where the end of your trail will be and hide a prize for the trail follower. The prize could be anything from an interesting stone to a whole picnic!

6. Get a friend or a grown-up to follow your trail. Can they follow it all the way to the end and find the prize you've left behind?

7. Take it in turns to make and follow a trail – what will you discover today?

Hints and tips:

- Try and put the end of your trail out of sight of the beginning – that makes it more exciting to follow!

- You can make your trail trickier by adding obstacles, different paths or dead ends.

Keep adventuring:

Try making a trail you can walk on, or one you can balance on, or one where you have to jump from thing to thing without touching the ground. Once you're a trail master why not try using your collection to build a maze?

Build a Big Bad Mouse Trap

The Gruffalo's Child is desperate to spot a Big Bad Mouse!
Are you brave enough to try and catch one?

Adventure kit:

- A stick
- A ball of string
- A spade
- Any small animal toy
- A flat bit of wood or
  a piece of bark
- A friend or a
  grown-up to play with

What to do:

1. Find a soft bit of ground, a sandpit or an empty flowerbed that you can dig in.

2. Use your spade to dig a shallow hole about the size of your hand.

3. Now measure your stick. It needs to be about the length of your arm from fingertip to elbow, so you might need to snap a bit off one end to make it the right size. Now tie one end of the string around the middle of your stick.

4. Take your flat piece of wood or bark and stand it on one side of the hole. This will be the roof of your trap. Put your stick on the other side and lean them towards each other over the hole until the stick is holding up the roof. This may take a bit of jiggling to get it to balance but keep trying.

5. Take the string in one hand and then take a few steps away from the trap, unrolling the string as you go, being careful not to make the stick wobble. You're now ready to capture a Big Bad Mouse!

6. First have a little practice. Get your friend or grown-up to walk your small animal toy along the ground until it falls into the hole . . .

7. Spring your trap! Pull sharply on the string. The stick should pop out from under the trap roof and the roof should fall and cover the hole, capturing the animal! If your toy doesn't quite fit in the hole you might need to dig it a bit deeper.

8. Reset your trap by re-balancing the trap roof on the stick. Take it in turns to spring the trap and catch all your toys. Now you'll be an expert catcher should the Big Bad Mouse ever pay you a visit!

Hints and tips:

- You can make your string super long so that you can hide behind a tree or a bush before springing the trap – that way the Big Bad Mouse won't see you!

- Check your trap roof isn't home to any bugs and beasties before you use it to catch anything.

Keep adventuring:

How else could you catch a mouse? Can you build a trap for a bigger animal? What could you use as bait?

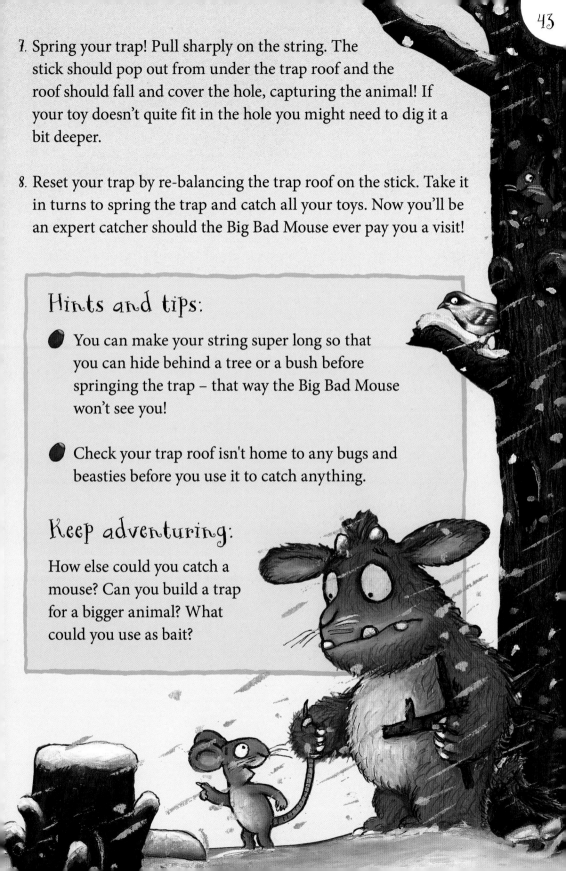

Garden Cupcakes

The Big Bad Mouse loves Gruffalo cake, but he has a monster appetite so he'll eat almost anything! If you want to catch a glimpse of him, why not try mixing up some garden goodies to tempt him out of his house?

Adventure Kit: Natural things to be your ingredients, a large bowl, a spoon, cupcake cases, an old cupcake baking tray or some plastic boxes.

What to do:

1. Gather your ingredients from your garden or park – dry leaves, grass cuttings, petals, sawdust, pine needles, herbs and soil are all great. Try to collect a variety of colours to make your cakes look extra yummy!

2. Use your hands to break up any bigger ingredients into small pieces and drop them into your mixing bowl.

3. Add some pinches of soil, grass or sawdust as you go.

4. Use your spoon to give everything a really good mix. If you are using herbs, give them a good bash with the spoon so they smell really good.

5. Use your spoon to transfer the mixture into your cake cases, box or tray. Use the back of the spoon to press the mixture into the corners.

6. Get creative with your cake decorations. Do you think the Big Bad Mouse would like sawdust curls, petals or soil sprinkles? Or maybe some of each!

7. See how many different cake varieties you can make. Will you have a chocolate mud cake or a rainbow petal surprise?

8. Leave your cakes somewhere outside for the Big Bad Mouse to find. Mice love cake!

Hints and tips:

- Remember to collect things that are on the ground rather than picking living flowers and plants.

- The Big Bad Mouse isn't a fussy eater, so you can always use some bits from the kitchen to add to your cakes too, as long as you check with your grown-up first. Porridge oats, cereal and dried herbs are all good for sprinkling and mixing – just remember that any pretend food you make outside is not for eating by people, only mice and monsters!

Keep adventuring:

If you don't fancy having a Big Bad Mouse in your garden, perhaps some of your toys would like to have a tea party instead? After all, everyone loves a tasty treat!

Make a Monster Mouse

"The Big Bad Mouse is terribly strong and his scaly tail is terribly long. His eyes are like pools of terrible fire and his terrible whiskers are tougher than wire."
What will your monster mouse look like?

Adventure Kit: Some air-drying clay, natural items, a scrap of cardboard.

What to do:

1. Think carefully about how you want your monster mouse to look and then gather some natural things from your garden or park. Will your monster mouse have stone teeth, stick claws or pine needle spikes?

2. Take a handful of clay and roll it into a ball for the mouse's body.

3. Take a smaller handful of clay and roll it into a ball for your mouse's head.

4. Push the head on to the body. You could use a stick pushed through both balls to hold them together if you like.

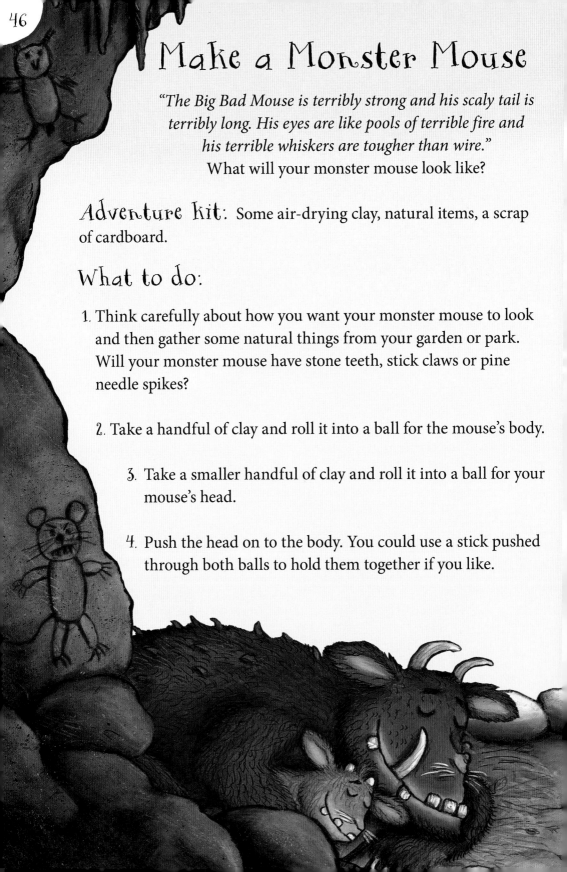

5. Pop your monster mouse on to a piece of cardboard so that it doesn't stick to the table.

6. While the clay is still soft, use the natural materials you've collected to give your monster mouse its features. Ears, a tail, whiskers, teeth and claws. Try different combinations of the things you have found to see which makes your mouse the most fearsome. How big and bad can you make your mouse?

Hints and tips:

- Leave your monster mouse overnight so that the clay goes dry and hard before you play with it. You could even paint your mouse once it's dry if you want to.

- If you don't have clay you could use playdough, salt dough or even some sticky mud!

Keep adventuring:

If you don't like the idea of your mouse being monstrous, you could always make a sweet little brown mouse instead! Once you've finished your mouse, why not try creating some of the other animals from the story too?

Shadow Adventures

The mouse isn't really so big and bad, but he is rather clever. He uses the light of the moon to make his shadow look like a terrible creature to scare away the Gruffalo's Child. Have a go at making your own shadow shapes!

Adventure Kit: A sunny day, your eyes.

What to do:

First find a smooth surface on which you can see your shadow. Stand with the sun behind you and hold out your hand until you can see its shadow on the ground in front of you. Now move your hand closer to the ground and then further away from the ground to see what happens to the shadow. Turn your hand this way and that, opening and closing your fingers to change the shape of the shadow.

Once you've found a good spot for shadow play, see if you can use your hand to make a shadow creature with a snappy mouth like a crocodile. Can you use your fingers to give your creature an eye, a beak or an ear? How many different shapes can you make?

Now try using both your hands to make a shadow creature. With two hands you might be able to give your creature wings, horns and even a tail!

Next try making shadows with your whole body.
Here are a few things you could try . . .

Can you give yourself tentacles?

Can you make your shadow look really big or super small?

Put both hands beside your ears to make them look really huge!

Can you make your body look like a rocket about to blast off, or an alien with two heads?

Hold your fingers above your head to give yourself horns, hair or antennae.

Hints and tips:

● Shadows are cast when light shines on an object. Light fills the area around the object but cannot pass through it, leaving an area of darkness. Quite often the shape of the shadow is very different from the object that has made it. Lots of very normal things make wonderfully weird shadows!

● There are lots of shadows around on a bright sunny day but it's also fun to use a torch in the dark to create shadows too!

Keep adventuring:

Once you have the hang of creating interesting shadows, find a friend so you can make even more amazing shapes. You could also play shadow tag where you chase around and jump on each other's shadows.

A Squash and a Squeeze

"Wise old man, won't you help me, please?
My house is a squash and a squeeze."

The little old lady is not happy – her house is too small, even for one. Whatever can she do? The wise old man knows just how to help and tells her to take in her hen, then her goat, then her pig and even her cow! With her house filled with noisy farm animals, it's even worse than before. But when the little old lady lets them all out again, she discovers that perhaps her house isn't such a squash and a squeeze after all – in fact, it's perfect for one!

Read on to discover how to decorate your own wise old man's walking stick, make some yummy hot chocolate for the pig and even practise being a bricklayer to build your own house.

Make a Walking Stick

Walking sticks aren't just for the wise old man! Sticks are great to take out on your adventures to help you walk, climb, poke and clear the path. Why not make yourself a special one?

Adventure kit:

- Sandpaper
- An old cloth
- Paints and a paintbrush
- A ball of string
- Safety scissors

What to do:

1. First go on a stick hunt to find your walking stick. It should be around the height of your armpit when you stand it on the floor, and be fairly straight. It will need a comfy spot for a handle and it should be firm and dry, so steer clear of crumbly bits and insect holes.

2. Give your stick a rub down with the cloth to remove any mud and leaves.

3. Now take your sandpaper, which helps to make things smooth, and use it to rub off any lumps and bumps and bits of broken bark. Then give your stick another dust down with the old cloth to get rid of any sawdust.

4. Now decide where your handle will go. Take your stick for a little walk to test out both ends and see which is the comfiest to hold.

5. Once you've decided which way up your stick will go it's time to make your handle. Tie one end of the string to the stick with a nice tight knot.

Then take the ball of string and let out a little at a time so you can wrap it around the stick, keeping the loops nice and close to each other. As you wrap the string around you will slowly move down the stick making the handle as you go.

6. When your handle is big enough for your hand to fit comfortably, cut the string, leaving a short tail. Finally, take the tail and tuck it under the last loop you made a few times and pull it tight.

7. Now grab your paints and get decorating. Leaving aside the string handle, give your walking stick a makeover and paint it in any colour or pattern you like. Will you paint rings of colour, long lines, stars or dots?

Hints and tips:

🌼 To make your colourful patterns waterproof, you might want to use outdoor paints, or put a coat of clear varnish over your decorations.

🌼 You could also use some more string or tape to attach feathers or strings of beads to the top of your walking stick.

Keep adventuring:

Now it's time to take your walking stick on an adventure. Will it take you to the top of the tallest mountain, help you cross a stream or simply make you the wisest person in your family?

Decorate an Egg

If a hen lays an egg on your fireside rug, then get decorating!
Or you could just grab a few from the fridge . . .

Adventure kit:

- 6 eggs
- Some interesting shaped flowers and leaves
- An old pair of tights
- Safety scissors
- A saucepan
- A hob
- A spoon
- Some onion skins
- An old towel

What to do:

1. Lay the tights out on a table and cut each leg into sections about 15cm long.

2. Lay out a section and place a flower in the middle. Run one of your eggs under the tap to make it wet and help the flower stick to it. Then place the egg on top of the flower.

3. Now put your finger on top of the egg and hold it down. Ask your grown-up to gather the edges of the tights up and over the egg and tie them together in a knot so that the flower stays in place.

4. Now do the same with another section of tights and another egg, trying a different flower or a leaf so you get a variety of patterns. Once all your eggs are ready and tied

up in tights, pop them into the saucepan. Add the onion skins and then some cold water so that the eggs are completely covered.

5. Ask your grown-up to boil your eggs on the hob for 20 minutes. Once they have boiled, your grown-up can carefully lift the eggs out of the pan with a big spoon and pop them onto the old towel to cool. Make sure not to touch your eggs until they are completely cool.

6. Once the eggs are cool, carefully cut them out of the old tights. Peel off the leaves and flowers and check out the amazing patterns you have on all your shells!

7. Dry your eggs gently with the old towel and they are ready to display!

Hints and tips:

🌸 You can use anything you can think of to decorate your eggs. Strawberry leaves, herbs and carrot tops all work well.

🌸 Take care that the eggs don't stain your table or worktop when they come out of the pot. Make sure they stay on the old towel.

Keep adventuring:

You can do the same thing using red cabbage instead of the onion skins – you get the same brilliant patterns but your eggs turn blue!

Build a Wall

"Wise old man, won't you help me please? My house is a squash and a squeeze".
Why not try some bricklaying and practise building your own house.
You can make it as roomy as you like!

Adventure kit:

- Some toy bricks or blocks that can get muddy
- Sand
- Mud
- Water
- A big old bowl to mix in
- A spoon
- A plastic knife
- Something flat to build on

What to do:

1. First make your building cement. Take the big bowl and add equal amounts of mud and sand. Mix them up together with your spoon and then add water a little at a time. You want the mixture to be sticky but not too wet.

2. Find a good flat place to build and lay out your materials. A paving slab or an old plank of wood is good for building on.

3. Take a brick in your hand and use the spoon to dollop a little cement onto one of the flat edges. Then use the plastic knife to spread the cement out so that it fully covers the edge. Imagine you are spreading butter and jam on some yummy toast!

4. Place this brick where you want it on your flat surface with the wet cement facing down. The brick should stick to the surface.

5. Spread cement on another brick and stick it next to the first one. You may also want to put cement between the ends of the two bricks so that they stick together too. Give the top of the bricks a couple of taps with the handle of your knife to make sure they are level.

6. Keep adding bricks to the line until you have five or six in a row. This is the first layer of your wall.

7. You can now start building upwards. Dollop a load of cement all over the top of your first layer and spread it out as before. Then take some more bricks and carefully squish them into the cement to make the second layer of your wall.

8. Now you have the hang of it, keep dolloping, spreading and brick laying until your wall is as high as you'd like it!

9. Once you have one wall, try adding more walls in a square to make your house. You could even add a roof by cutting a spare piece of cardboard to the right size!

Hints and tips:

🍀 Pick through your mud and take out any big roots and stones before you start mixing, then your cement will be lovely and smooth!

🍀 If you don't have toy bricks you can use, try building a wall by cementing small rocks and pebbles together instead.

Keep adventuring:

Once your wall is complete, take your toys outside to try it out. Can they climb it, walk along it and balance on the top? When you've finished playing with it, why not try knocking it down? Then, when you've had enough building, get some water out and enjoy giving your bricks a good scrub to make them all shiny and clean again! If you scrape the cement off the bricks with your plastic knife, you can even save it to play with another day.

Piggy Hot Chocolate

The pig is always raiding the larder, so why not
make him something to fill his tummy!

Adventure kit:

- An old mug
- A spoon
- Some dry soil
- A jug of water
- Some washing-up
  liquid
- A big bowl
- A whisk
- Some small sticks

What to do:

1. Take your mug and put in three or four heaped spoonfuls of dry soil.

2. Use your jug to add water to your mug a little at a time, stirring well with your spoon after each addition. Keep stirring until the soil has turned the water a lovely chocolatey brown. If your mixture is too thin, add more soil. If it's too thick, add more water. Fill your mug about three quarters of the way up.

3. Next you need to prepare your frothy milk. Take the bowl and add a nice big squeeze of washing-up liquid to the bottom. Then pour in a small amount of water. Now take the whisk (or a good mixing stick) and whisk the water and washing-up liquid together nice and fast, like you are beating an egg. You may need to add a little more water, but keep mixing until you have lots of lovely white foamy bubbles. This will be your frothy milk!

4. Use the spoon to scoop the milk froth from the bowl and into your chocolate mud-filled mug. Fill the mug to the top and then pile on a little more froth to make it look like whipped cream.

5. Rub a little soil between your hands to make it really fine and powdery and then sprinkle it over your milky mug. Now it will look like you've dusted it with chocolate shavings. Yummy!

6. Finally find a good-sized stick to pop into your mug to look like a chocolate flake. What pig could resist?

Hints and tips:

✿ If your milky bubbles start to look a bit flat, just give them another whisk to perk them up again!

✿ Remember that this hot chocolate is only for story animals, so don't drink any, no matter how delicious it looks!

Keep adventuring:

Think about how you could make your mug even more piggy – could you add some tasty leaf decorations or find something to look like melty marshmallows? If you have more than one cup, you can make a whole tray of yummy hot drinks. If you have just the one then pour your hot chocolate out in a flowerbed for a pig to snuffle up and get busy making another cup.

Make an Animal Pen

"My nose has a tickle and there's no room to sneeze.
My house is a squash and a squeeze."
There's no room in the little old lady's house with all her animals inside,
so why not build them their own outdoor pens to live in?

Adventure kit: Four sticks about as long as your forearm, lots of
little sticks and some big leaves, and some farmyard animal toys.

What to do:

1. Find a good place to build your pen, brush away any leaves and then
   place the four long sticks on the ground to make a square.

2. Take a small stick and push it into the ground in one corner of the square
   so that it stands up by itself. Then, using a side of your square as a guide,
   keep pushing sticks into the ground in a straight line to create a fence.
   This is the first side of your pen.

3. Now build two more sides of your pen in the same way using the stick
   square as your guide.

4. Your pen will now have three sides, so next make a gate. Take a leaf and
   thread it onto a stick by pushing the stick up through one corner of the
   leaf and down through another corner, like you are sewing.

5. Position your gate on the last side of your pen by pushing the stick gatepost into the ground. The leaf should move backwards and forwards on its post so you can open and close the gate.

6. Push some sticks into the ground on either side of your gate to complete your square pen.

7. Once your pen is finished and you are sure there are no gaps through which animals can escape, grab your toys and let them make themselves at home.

Hints and tips:

🌸 If the ground is really hard, try watering the area you want to use before you start, using pebbles for your fence in place of sticks or playing in a sand pit instead!

🌸 You can push in the sticks side by side or you can leave a space between each one and weave long bits of grass in and out of each stick to create your fence.

Keep adventuring:

Now you have the hang of it, you can build pens in triangles, circles or even star shapes! Once your animals are safely in their pens, they'll need some food and water to keep them happy. Can you find some lush green grass to feed them? Might your animals like some rocks to climb, or some soft moss to lie down on?

Catch a Flea

The little old lady is tearing her hair out, and to add
to the chaos the goat has fleas! Fleas hop everywhere.
Try this game and see if you can catch one!

Adventure kit: A long, stiff piece of grass, your jumping legs, your catching hands and someone to play with!

What to do:

First find something to be your flea. A long, stiff bit of grass with a
tufty end works best. Find one that touches the floor when you hold the
end of the stalk with your hand out in front of you.

Now imagine that the flea is the tufty end of your long bit of grass.
Holding the other end, practise making your flea hop about from one
thing to another. Can you make him do tiny hops, giant jumps and
ginormous leaps?

Next decide who will control the flea and who will be the catcher. The
aim of the game is for the catcher to catch the flea and for the flea to
keep jumping free!